Sly Fox
and Red Hen

Illustrated by Diana Mayo

Red Hen lived in a
little house in a tree.

Level 2 is ideal for children who have received some reading instruction and can read short, simple sentences with help.

Special features:

Frequent repetition of main story words and phrases

Short, simple sentences

Sly Fox picked up his black bag.

"I'm going to catch Red Hen and eat her," he said.

10

11

Large, clear type

Careful match between story and pictures

"I will catch you," said Sly Fox, and he ran round and round and round.

16

17

Educational Consultant:
Geraldine Taylor

A catalogue record for this book is available from the British Library

Published by Ladybird Books Ltd
80 Strand, London, WC2R 0RL
A Penguin Company

4 6 8 10 9 7 5 3
© LADYBIRD BOOKS LTD MMX
Ladybird, Read It Yourself and the Ladybird Logo are registered or
unregistered trade marks of Ladybird Books Limited.

ISBN: 978-1-40930-392-3

Printed in China

Sly Fox lived in the wood.
And he was hungry.

Sly Fox picked up
his black bag.

"I'm going to catch
Red Hen and eat her,"
he said.

Sly Fox hid in Red Hen's little house.

"I'm the Fox, I'm the Fox, I'm really sly. You can't beat me, however you try!" said Sly Fox.

Red Hen saw Sly Fox and jumped up out of his way.

"You're the Fox, you're the Fox, you're really sly. But you won't catch me, however you try!" said Red Hen.

15

"I will catch you," said
Sly Fox, and he ran
round and round
and round.

17

Red Hen's head went
round and round, too.
She fell down into
Sly Fox's big black bag.

19

Sly Fox ran into the wood.
The big black bag was
heavy, and Sly Fox sat
down to rest. Then he
fell asleep.

Red Hen jumped out of the bag.

"You're the Fox, you're the Fox, you're really sly. But you won't catch me, however you try!" said Red Hen.

Red Hen put some heavy stones in the bag. Then she ran all the way home.

Sly Fox tipped the bag into the cooking pot.

"I'm the Fox, I'm the Fox, I'm really sly. I will eat you. Say goodbye!"

The stones fell
SPLASH!
into the hot water.

"Ouch!" said Sly Fox.
"I really hate that hen!"

How much do you remember about the story of Sly Fox and Red Hen? Answer these questions and find out!

- Where does Red Hen live?

- Where does Sly Fox live?

- How does Sly Fox catch Red Hen?

- What does Red Hen put in the bag?